Deerfield Public Library
920 Waukegan Road
Deerfield, Illinois 60015

W9-BZV-694

WITHDRAWN

JUL 1 7 1989

Rise and Shine

Fiona French

Little, Brown and Company

Boston   Toronto   London

Rise and shine,
And give God the glory, glory,
Children of the Lord.

The Lord said to Noah,
"There's gonna be a floody, floody.
Get those children out of the muddy, muddy."
Children of the Lord.

The Lord said to Noah,
"Build me an arky, arky.

Build it out of hickory barky, barky."
Children of the Lord.

So Noah, he built him, he built him
An arky, arky.
Built it out of hickory barky, barky.
Children of the Lord.

The animals, the animals,
They came in by twosy, twosy.

Elephants and kangaroosie, oosie.
Children of the Lord.

It rained, it poured for forty daysy, daysy.

Nearly drove those poor animals
crazy, crazy.
Children of the Lord.

Then Noah, he sent out, he sent out
The dovey, dovey.
"Bring back the branch of lovey, lovey."
Children of the Lord.

The sun came out and dried up the landy, landy.
Everything was fine and dandy, dandy.
Children of the Lord.

The animals, the animals,
They came out by threesie, threesie.

Seems they'd heard about the birds and beesy, beesy.
Children of the Lord.

If you get to heaven before I doosie, doosie,
Tell St. Peter "Don't be so choosy, choosy."
Children of the Lord.

This is the end of, the end of my story, story.
Hope you found it hunky-dory, dory,
Children of the Lord.